Look at me! Look at me!

by Rose Williamson

TOP THAT

Licensed exclusively to Top That Publishing Ltd
Tide Mill Way, Woodbridge, Suffolk, IP12 1AP, UK
www.topthatpublishing.com
Copyright © 2013 Tide Mill Media
All rights reserved
2 4 6 8 9 7 5 3
Manufactured in China

Illustrated by Doreen Marts
Written by Rose Williamson

ISBN 978-1-78244-218-9

A catalogue record for this book is available from the British Library

Cammy Chameleon lived in a tree and was very good at hiding. Cammy turned brown on a brown branch and green on a green leaf.

It made it very easy to sneak up on yummy bugs!

But Cammy didn't want to hide. She thought she was a very beautiful chameleon indeed and she wanted all of the other animals to look at her.

She called out to the tree frogs, 'Look at me! Look at me!'

But the tree frogs could not see a green chameleon on a green leaf.

She called out to the lemurs,
'Look at me! Look at me!'

But the lemurs could not see a brown
chameleon on a brown branch.

Cammy was very upset that no one could see her. She began to wonder what it would be like if she didn't always blend in ...

Cammy climbed down from her tree and concentrated very, very hard ...

And turned red!

'Look at me! Look at me!'
she called to the tree frogs.
'What a beautiful chameleon!' they said.

Cammy practised changing colour all day.
She was pink on a grey stone ...

She was black on yellow sand ...

She was purple on an orange flower ...

... and orange on a purple flower.

'Look at me! Look at me!' she called to the lemurs. 'What a beautiful chameleon!' they said.

Cammy thought that she was the most beautiful chameleon in the whole world.

Soon, she began to feel hungry and went home to her tree.

Cammy climbed onto her brown branch and waited for a yummy bug. She waited and waited.

She watched the other chameleons catching bugs on their sticky tongues and her stomach rumbled. She was very hungry!

Then, Cammy saw a group of bugs nearby! But, before she could stick out her long tongue, they saw her beautiful colours and flew away!

'What a beautiful chameleon!'
the laughing bugs called to her.

Suddenly, Cammy felt very silly.
A colourful chameleon couldn't hide
like a plain brown chameleon!

Cammy knew that to catch bugs,
she would need to blend in so she
concentrated very, very hard ...

and changed colour so that she
blended in with her surroundings!

Cammy had learnt that it is not good to show off and was happy being a regular chameleon again.

But sometimes, just every once in a while,
Cammy concentrates very, very hard ...

Write the sound.

m

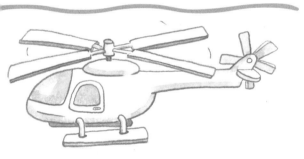

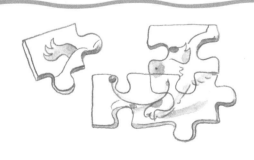

Identify and write the letters that represent initial sounds in words.

1

Write the sound.

....

....

....

....

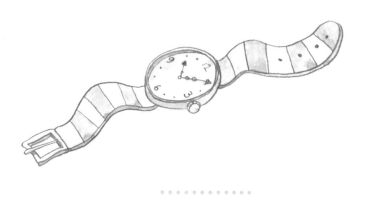

....

....

....

....

Identify and write the letters that represent initial sounds in wo

Write the sound.

. . . .

. . . .

. . . .

> **Invitation**
> Please come to my
> party on Saturday
> at 2 o'clock.
> From Pat

. . . .

. . . .

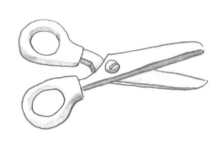

. . . .

. . . .

. . . .

Identify and write the letters that represent initial sounds in words.

③

Write the sound.

. . . .

. . . .

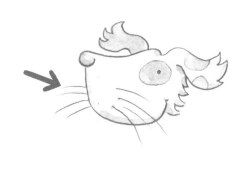

. . . .

. . . .

. . . .

. . . .

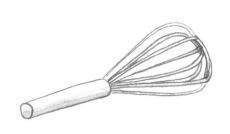

. . . .

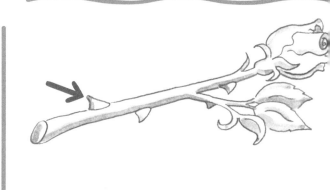

. . . .

Identify and write the letters that represent initial sounds in wo

Write the sound. Write the word.

c   **d**   **z**   **v**

c a t

_____

h   **m**   **f**   **p**

_ a n

....

_ a t

_ a n

....

Identify and write the letters that represent initial sounds in words.

(5)

b   d   h   j

_ o g   _ o p

k   l   m   p

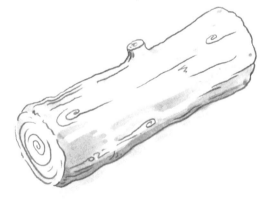

_ o g   _ o p

Identify and write the letters that represent initial sounds in wor

r   h

_en

n   s

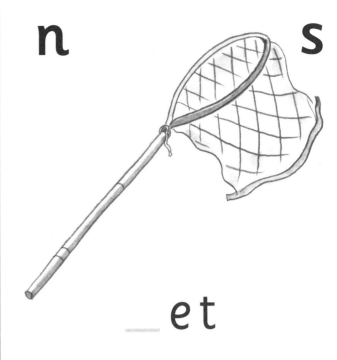

_et

· ·

m   x

_en

y   v

_et

· ·

Identify and write the letters that represent initial sounds in words.

7

Write the sound. Write the word.

j   t   z   s

_ u g

_ u n

....

m   w   b   d

_ u g

_ u n

....

Identify and write the letters that represent initial sounds in wo

Write the sound. Write the word.

p   g

_ig

....

w   b

_in

....

t   w

_ig

....

g   t

_in

....

Identify and write the letters that represent initial sounds in words.

Match

ba

bo

ha

ho

la

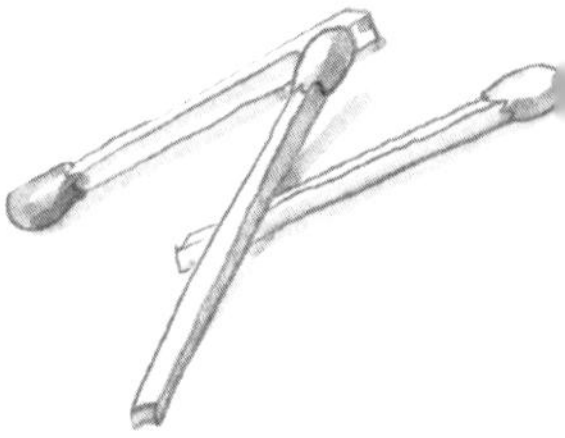

lo

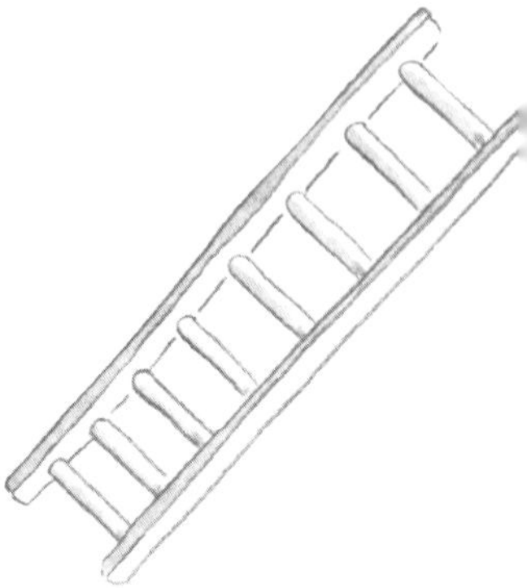

ma

mo

Read a consonant-vowel blend in the initial position.

he

hu

ne

nu

je

ju

te

tu

Read a consonant-vowel blend in the initial position.

bi

pi

be

pe

li

wi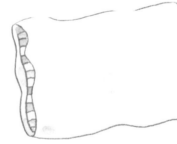

le

we

Read a consonant-vowel blend in the initial position.

Write the sound. Write the word.

p   s

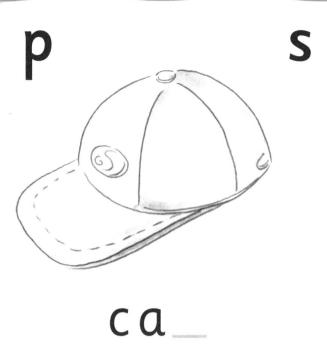

c a __

. . . .

t   p

c o __

. . . .

g   d

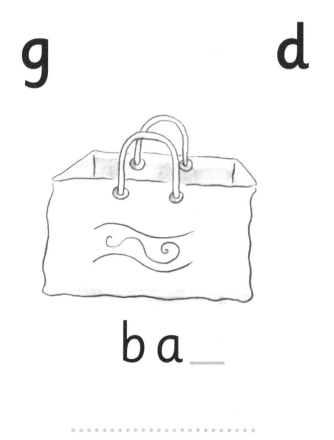

b a __

. . . .

x   s

f o __

. . . .

Identify and write the letters that represent final sounds in words.

x   n | s   b

te_

bu_

....

p   b | d   r

we_

su_

....

14

Identify and write the letters that represent final sounds in words.

t   d   b   d

h u __   b i __

m   g   y   x

r u __   s i __

Identify and write the letters that represent final sounds
in words.

15

Write the word.

cat

cot

cut

dig

dug

dog

........cat........

....

hut

hat

hit

bid

bed

bud

....

....

Identify vowels in the middle of words.
Blend and read simple regular words.

Write the word.

pan

pin

pen

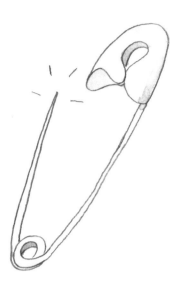

....

pet

pat

pot

....

big

bag

beg

....

nut

not

net

....

Identify vowels in the middle of words.
Blend and read simple regular words.

Match the rhyme.

hen

mug

Identify words that rhyme.

Match the rhyme.

van

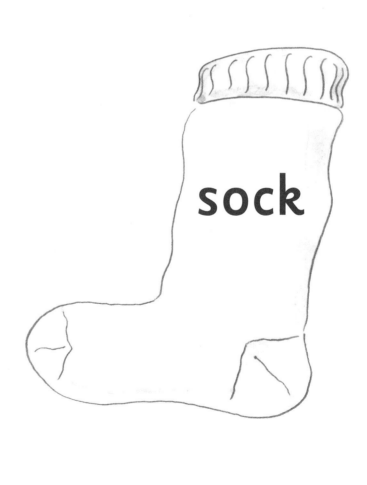
sock

Rhyming words.

hat   _an   _ag   _ap

cat   pan   rag   lap

cat   rhyming   words

<p>ot   _od   _og   _op

got   pod   jog   pop

Blend and read simple regular words. Identify words that rhyme.
Write simple rhyming words.

21

Write rhyming words.

s un   _ ug   _ ut   _ ub

nun   hug   but   cub

· ·

Blend and read simple regular words. Identify words that rhyme.
Write simple rhyming words.

net   _en   _ed   _eg

wet   men   fed   beg

....

Blend and read simple regular words. Identify words that rhyme.
Write simple rhyming words.

23

Write rhyming words.

b in   _ip   _ix   _ig

fin   hip   fix   fig

Blend and read simple regular words. Identify words that rhyme
Write simple rhyming words.